Monkey Puzzle
MAKE AND DO BOOK

Based on the picture book by
Julia Donaldson • Axel Scheffler

MACMILLAN CHILDREN'S BOOKS

Hints and Tips to Read With a Grown-Up

Are you ready to get creative? There are lots of fun ideas in this book for brilliant things to make and do. Before you get started, read through these hints and tips with a grown-up.

🍃 Have a grown-up with you at all times when doing any of the activities in this book, and make sure you ask for help if you find any of the steps a bit tricky.

🍃 Be very careful when using scissors, and always check with a grown-up first to make sure they're not too sharp and are safe for you to use.

🍃 Before you start an activity, read the instructions together so you can make sure you have everything you need.

🍃 Some of these craft ideas can get messy, so wear an apron or old clothes that your grown-up doesn't mind you getting dirty. It's a good idea to tie your hair back if it's long to stop it getting in the way.

🍃 It's best to work on a wipe-clean surface, but you could always cover the floor and table with used newspapers or an old cloth, too.

🍃 Remember to wash your hands after using paint, glue or anything else that might make a mess.

🍃 Arts and crafts can be a great way to reuse things that you might otherwise throw away. For example, you could cut up an old cereal box instead of buying new card. On the next page, you can see a list of some things you might need for the activities in this book. Why not ask your friends and family to help you start saving them?

Things to collect:

Cereal boxes
Lolly sticks
Leftover wool, string and ribbon
Egg cartons

Fallen leaves and sticks
Pebbles
Leftover tissue paper

How to use your templates:

You can find some drawings on the back of your sticker pages that you can use to make templates that will help you with some of the activities in this book, like the Paper Leaves on page 27. Here's how to make your templates:

1 Lay a piece of thin paper or tracing paper over the outline on the back of your sticker page. Draw over it with a pencil.

2 Carefully cut out your drawing and glue it to a piece of card.

3 Now cut around your drawing so that you have a piece of card the same shape as the original outline. This is your template! You can draw around it as many times as you like.

How to use your stickers:

There are two pages of stickers at the end of this book. They have been specially designed for you to decorate the things you make, but you might prefer to draw your own decorations.

Now you're all set to start – so roll up your sleeves, get out your pens and pencils and have fun!

Elephant Mask

"My mum isn't a great grey hunk.
She hasn't got tusks or a curly trunk."
The elephant does! Make your own great grey elephant mask.

You will need:

A paper plate
Safety scissors
Paints
A paintbrush
2 A4 sheets of card
Glue
A length of elastic

What to do:

1 Ask a grown-up to cut eyeholes in your paper plate so you'll be able to see when you wear your mask.

2 Paint the plate grey and leave to dry.

3 Cut two ear shapes from one sheet of card, and a trunk from the second sheet. Paint them grey and add some dark grey wrinkles to the trunk. Leave to dry.

4 Glue your ears either side of your mask, then glue the trunk in the middle.

5 Paint two white tusks either side of the trunk. Leave to dry.

6 Ask your grown-up to pierce a hole on either side of the mask, just above the ears.

You could use a hole punch if you have one.

7 Thread the elastic through the holes and ask your grown-up to adjust the mask for you so it fits around your head. Then tie the ends of the elastic in tight knots to secure.

Tips, Tricks and Twists

🍃 Why not paint a paper plate red and add a beak to make a parrot mask? You could decorate it with feathers, too.

🍃 You could make other animal masks for your friends and act out a story!

Pipe Cleaner Pencil Toppers

"And anyway, her tail coils round trees!"
These cute monkeys have bendy tails that coil around your pens and pencils!

You will need:

Brown pipe cleaners
  (4 per monkey)
Pink paper
Safety scissors
Glue
A black pen

What to do:

1 Hold three pipe cleaners parallel to each other so their ends line up. Twist them together in the middle to secure.

2 Pull the ends apart as shown. These will become your monkey's head, arms, legs and tail.

3 Tightly wrap the fourth pipe cleaner around the twist you have made – this will be your monkey's body.

4 About 1cm from the end of a leg, bend the pipe cleaner back on itself. Bend again to make a foot, as shown. Repeat with the other leg.

If you don't have brown pipe cleaners, you could make multicolour monkeys instead!

5 About 1cm from the end of an arm, bend the pipe cleaner back on itself. Bend the short piece in half to make a hand, as shown. Repeat with the other hand.

6 Bend your remaining top strand into an oval shape for the head, and twist it around at the bottom to hold it in place.

7 Cut a small oval from the pink paper and draw on a face. You can draw eyes or use stickers from your sticker sheet.

8 Glue the face on to your monkey's head. Cut out and glue on small ears too, to stick out from behind the head.

9 Twist your remaining bottom strand into a long curly tail.

10 Now bend your monkey's tail, arms or legs around a pen or a pencil!

Tips, Tricks and Twists

🍃 Why not make a whole monkey family? Just cut your pipe cleaners a little shorter to make a smaller baby monkey.

🍃 Cut a tree out of cardboard, or find a large twig outside, and coil your monkeys around it so they look like they are clinging on to jungle branches.

🍃 Can you make any other pipe cleaner animals? How about twisting two different colours together to make a coiling snake, or cutting a pipe cleaner into shorter lengths then bending them to make wiggly caterpillars?

Handprint Animals

Make amazing symmetrical handprint pictures of jungle animals!

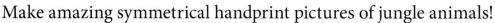

You will need:

Paints
Paintbrushes
A4 paper
Felt-tip pens

Parrot

'Symmetrical' means that both sides are the same!

1 Fold a sheet of paper in half so the short sides meet, then open it out again.

2 Use a paintbrush to paint your palm, thumb and first finger red. Then paint yellow on to your third and fourth fingers and blue on your little finger.

3 Keeping your fingers together, press your hand on to one half of the paper.

4 Quickly take your hand off and use your other hand to fold the paper along the fold line again. Press down and rub your clean hand over the paper.

5 Open to reveal your symmetrical handprint shape! When the paint has dried, paint or draw on the parrot's head, eyes and beak, and add feet at the bottom.

Don't forget to wash your hands after making your print.

Spider

1 Fold a sheet of paper in half so the short sides meet, then open it out again.

2 Paint a thick layer of black paint over your palm and fingers, leaving the thumbs clean.

3 Keeping your fingers wide, press your hand on to one half of the card.

4 Quickly take your hand off and use your other hand to fold the paper along the fold line again. Press down and rub your clean hand over the paper.

5 Open to reveal your shape! When the paint has dried, add eyes and draw on a smiley mouth.

You could add fingerprint flies too.

Tips, Tricks and Twists

🍃 If you prefer, use your stickers instead of drawing the animals' eyes.

🍃 Make sure you put a nice thick layer of paint on your hand so you make a solid print.

🍃 Can you make any other splodgy handprint pictures? What about a butterfly or a colourful jungle flower?

Butterfly Wings

Butterfly flies around the jungle helping the little monkey find his mum. Flutter around just like him with your very own pair of butterfly wings!

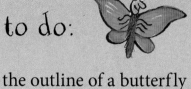

You will need:

3 A4 sheets of card
A pencil
Safety scissors
Glue
Paints
Paintbrushes
A 1m length of ribbon

What to do:

1 Draw the outline of a butterfly wing in pencil on a sheet of card, then carefully cut it out.

2 Lay the wing on a second sheet of card and draw around it. Cut it out so you have two wings.

3 Paint both wings blue. Before the paint dries, add a little white paint to the straight edge of each wing, then use a clean paintbrush to gently spread the white paint across the wings, so that the colour gradually goes from light to dark.

4 When dry, paint a black and white pattern on the shaped edges of your wings and leave to dry. You can copy the picture.

5 Turn your wings over and paint the other side in the same way.

6 Draw an oval on your third piece of card, about 10cm wide and 20cm long, then cut it out.

7 Paint one side of your oval brown with black and yellow stripes and leave to dry. This is your butterfly's body!

You could cut up an empty cereal box to use instead of card.

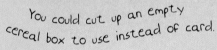

8 Spread a strip of glue about 1cm wide down the straight edge of each wing and stick the body on to the wings.

9 Ask a grown-up to pierce two holes on each side of the body.

10 Thread your ribbon through the top two holes from the front, then bring the ends back through the bottom two holes as shown.

11 This will mean you have two big loops to put your arms through. Try your wings on, and ask your grown-up to pull the two ends of the ribbon so that the wings fit you. Tie the ends in a double knot and trim off the extra ribbon. Now your wings are ready to wear!

Make sure the ribbon isn't too tight, so you can take your wings on and off easily.

I wish I had wings like these!

Tips, Tricks and Twists

🍃 You could paint your butterfly wings any colour you like, or add extra decorations like biodegradable glitter, sequins or stickers from your sticker page.

🍃 Why not dress up as a parrot instead? Cut your card into the shape of parrot wings, and paint them bright red, yellow and blue.

You might find it helpful to copy this picture.

Slithering Snake Puppet

"Mum doesn't look a bit like this. She doesn't slither about and hiss."
Who slithers and hisses? The snake! Make your own slithering snake puppet.

You will need:

2 sheets of A4 coloured
  paper
Safety scissors
Glue
Colouring pens or
  pencils
2 lolly sticks
Sticky tape
A small piece of red
  paper

What to do:

1 Fold your sheets of A4 paper in half lengthways, then in half lengthways again. Cut along the folds so each sheet becomes four long strips.

2 Glue the end of one strip on top of another strip at a right angle, so you have an L shape.

3 Fold your first piece of paper over your second.

4 Now fold your second piece back over your first. Keep going in this way, folding the strips back over one another.

5 When you reach the end of your paper strips, glue on two more strips and keep folding, to make your snake longer.

Try using different coloured strips so you make a pattern as you fold.

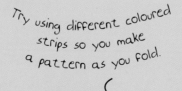

6 Trim one end of your paper body to make a pointed tail. Cut the other end into a rounded head shape.

7 Draw two eyes on to your snake's head, and add two dots to make a nose.

8 Draw a pointy forked tongue on your piece of red paper and cut it out. Stick it to your snake's head, just underneath the nose.

9 Use sticky tape to fasten a lolly stick under your snake's head, and another under its tail. Now hold a stick in each hand and make your snake slither and wriggle!

Tips, Tricks and Twists

🍃 Decorate both sides of your paper strips before you fold them all together to give your snake amazing patterns!

🍃 You could add stickers from your sticker sheet or googly eyes for your snake's face.

🍃 Keep adding more folded strips of paper to make your snake super-long. How long and wriggly can you go?

Monkey Pop-up Card

Why not make a special pop-up card for your grown-up or a birthday card for a friend? Maybe the little monkey should make one for his mum!

You will need:

3 sheets of A4 card: pink, green and white
A ruler
Safety scissors
Glue
Colouring pens or pencils

What to do:

1 Fold the green card in half so the short sides meet.

2 Keeping the card folded, make two 5cm parallel cuts near the centre of the folded edge, about 5cm apart.

3 Open the card and push out the little box made by your cuts. Crease the fold on the box so it pops out from the rest of the card.

4 On the white card, draw and colour in a small picture of a monkey to pop up when the card is opened.

5 Cut out your monkey and glue the bottom half to the front of the pop-up box, as shown in the picture.

Don't glue anything to the top of your pop-up box or your picture won't pop up properly!

6 Take your pink card and fold it in half so the short sides meet.

7 Glue the green sheet of card inside the pink sheet.

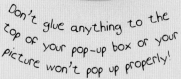

8 Decorate the inside of your card – why not try the leaf prints from page 26?

9 Now draw a picture on the front of your card and write a message. How about "Have a jolly jungle birthday" or "To the world's best mum"?

Tips, Tricks and Twists

🍃 Don't forget to write who the card is to on the inside, and to say that it's from you!

🍃 It doesn't have to be a monkey – how about Butterfly or another jungle animal?

🍃 Why not decorate an envelope to match? Then put your card in the envelope and write who it's for on the front.

Pasta Pictures

Use paints and pens to turn pasta shapes
into colourful jungle animals.

You will need:

Dried pasta in
    different shapes
A4 sheets of card
Glue
Paints
A paintbrush
Felt-tip pens

Beautiful Butterflies

1 Paint a few pasta bows any colour you like.
   Once they're dry, glue them to a sheet of card.
   Make sure they're not too close together.

2 When the glue has dried, use paints and felt-tip
   pens to add spots, stripes or other patterns
   to turn your bows into beautiful butterflies.

3 Finish off by drawing a pair of antennae with a
   black pen on the card at the top of each butterfly.

Hello, friend!

Slithery Snake

1 Paint six pasta tubes brown. When the paint has dried,
   glue the tubes in a long, wiggly line to make a snake.

2 Once the glue has dried, paint on a pattern of black spots.

3 Now give your snake a face! Add eyes
   from your sticker sheet, then use a red
   pen to draw a forked tongue on the card.

Brilliant Bugs

1 Paint a few pasta shells any colour you like. Once they're dry, glue them to a sheet of card, not too close together.

2 When the glue has dried, use paints and felt tip pens to turn the shells into brilliant bugs. How about making a stripy bug, a spotty one, or making up your own design?

3 Finish off by drawing some legs and antennae with a black pen.

You could even stick on some googly eyes.

Tips, Tricks and Twists

🍃 These look brilliant if you paint a jungle scene on your card before you stick down the pasta shapes, so your butterflies can flutter through a blue sky and your bugs can sit on bright green leaves. Don't forget to let the paint dry first!

🍃 Can you think of any other pasta shapes that you could turn into creatures? Try macaroni caterpillars or a spider with spaghetti legs.

Wiggling Caterpillar

". . . None of my babies looks like me."
Butterfly's babies are little wiggly caterpillars! How about making one of your own?

You will need:

An egg carton
Safety scissors
Wool
Red and yellow paint
A paintbrush
Felt-tip pens

What to do:

Hello there! Nice day day for a wiggle!

1 Ask a grown-up to cut the egg carton so you have six individual egg holders.

2 Paint the outside of each egg holder yellow with a red bottom. Let the paint dry.

3 Ask your grown-up to poke two holes in the bottom of each egg holder, then thread wool through each one as shown.

4 Tie a knot and cut the ends short to make furry bristles for your caterpillar.

5 Ask your grown-up to poke a hole in each side of four of the egg holders, and a single hole in one side of the remaining two. These two egg holders will be your caterpillar's head and tail.

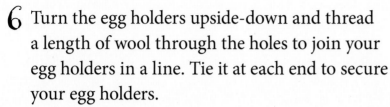

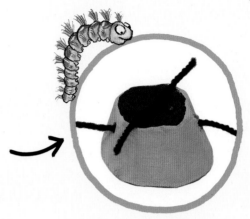

6 Turn the egg holders upside-down and thread a length of wool through the holes to join your egg holders in a line. Tie it at each end to secure your egg holders.

7 Draw a face on the egg holder at one end – this will be your caterpillar's head.

8 Now move your caterpillar and watch it wiggle!

Tips, Tricks and Twists

🍃 Try threading more egg holders on to make an extra-long caterpillar.

🍃 Add a leaf made from green paper for your caterpillar to sit on. Cut a bite-shaped hole to make it look like it's been snacking!

🍃 You could use stickers instead of drawing your caterpillar's eyes, and add any other decorations you like.

Paper Butterflies

Try two different ways to make a whole host of colourful jungle butterflies!

Butterfly Paper Chains

You can use the template on the back of your sticker sheet!

You will need:

A4 paper
A pencil
Safety scissors
Crayons or coloured
pencils

What to do:

1 Fold the paper in half so the short sides meet, then in half again, then once more.

2 Draw a simple butterfly shape on top of your folded paper. Make sure to draw the wings all the way to the edges of the paper.

3 Keep your paper folded and cut out around the outline you have drawn. Don't cut around the edges of the wings where they meet the folds, or you'll cut through your paper chain!

4 Carefully unfold the paper. Now you've got two rows of butterflies! Decorate your butterflies with colourful patterns.

Stick your paper chains together and hang them up.

Fluttering Butterflies

You will need:

Tissue paper
A clothes peg
Felt-tip pens
A pipe cleaner
Glue
A length of wool

What to do:

1 Clip a rectangle of tissue paper in the middle of the clothes peg to make your butterfly's wings.

2 Draw your butterfly's face on the peg with a felt-tip pen, or use your stickers.

3 Bend a pipe cleaner into a U shape and curl the ends. Glue the pipe cleaner under the peg so the antennae stick out from the butterfly's face.

4 Tie the wool around the back of the clothes peg. Hold the other end of the wool and run. Watch your butterfly fly!

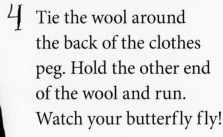

Tips, Tricks and Twists

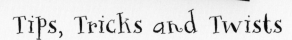

Use blue paper to make your butterflies look like the one from *Monkey Puzzle*!

Draw other animals on to folded paper to make different paper chains. Remember to always draw up to the fold so your animals stay joined together.

Guess the Animal Game

"Let's have a think. How big is she?"
Make this jungle guessing game to play with a friend!

You will need:

2 sheets of green A4 card
2 sheets of white A4 card
A ruler
A pencil
Safety scissors
A sheet of A4 paper
Colouring pens or pencils
Glue

What to do:

1 Ask a grown-up to help you use the ruler and pencil to divide a piece of white card into six roughly equal sections along the long side and three along the short side. Cut along the pencil lines to make 18 small rectangles.

2 Do the same with your second piece of white card. You will end up with 36 pieces.

3 Draw pencil lines on your sheet of paper in the same way you did in step 1. Draw a jungle animal in 12 of the rectangles and colour them in. You can copy or trace the animals on the back of your sticker sheet.

4 Ask your grown-up to photocopy the sheet of paper so you have three sets of 12 pictures.

You can decorate your boards, too! Try the leaf prints from page 26.

5 Cut along the pencil lines and stick the pictures on to your pieces of card.

6 Take one set of 12 cards and fold back the bottom 1cm to make a tab. Glue them to a sheet of green card in three lines.

7 Repeat step 6 to make a second board, but make sure you put the animals in a different order.

8 The remaining 12 cards stay loose. Now you're ready to play!

How to play:

1 Each player gets a board. Put the 12 loose cards face down. Each player takes one card, making sure the other player doesn't see the animal on it.

2 Take it in turns to ask questions about the other player's animal. For example, 'Does it have fur?' The other player can only answer 'yes' or 'no'.

3 The asking player can fold down all their cards that the answer rules out. For example, if they say 'no' to the animal having fur, the asking player can fold down all the animals that have fur. If they say 'yes', the asking player can fold down all the animals that do not have fur.

4 Take it in turns asking questions and folding the cards down, until you think you can guess which animal it is. Each player can only guess once! If they guess correctly, they win, but if their guess is wrong, the other player wins.

Jungle Wind Chimes

Make these jingly jangly wind chimes that will make noises in the breeze!

You will need:

8 bamboo canes
(various lengths
between 5cm and
20cm)
Garden twine or
string
Safety scissors
Washi tape or sticky
tape
A stick (about 40cm
long)
Plain paper
Colouring pens or
pencils
Green tissue paper

If your bamboo canes need to be cut to different sizes, make sure a grown-up does this for you.

What to do:

1 Cut a long length of twine and tightly wrap the middle section several times around the top of your longest piece of bamboo. Leave two lengths of twine, one on each side of the top of your bamboo cane.

2 Wrap your tape around the twine several times to hold it in place.

3 Wrap the lengths of twine around the top of your long stick, close to one end. Tie to secure them.

4 Repeat steps 1 to 3 with your next longest piece of bamboo, tying it to the stick around 4–5cm from the first piece. Continue until you have tied on all your bamboo, keeping the pieces evenly spaced along the stick.

5 Draw and colour four jungle flowers and four minibeasts on your paper, or use your stickers.

6 Cut out your flowers and minibeasts and ask a grown-up to poke a small hole in the top of each one.

7 Thread a length of twine through the hole in one of your pictures and knot it. Wrap the other end around the bottom of a bamboo cane and wrap tape over it, as in step 2.

Where will you hang your wind chimes?

8 Repeat step 7 with the rest of your pictures, so each bamboo cane has a different picture hanging from it.

9 Twist lengths of green tissue paper to make jungle vines and wrap them around your stick. Cut out and add some leaves, too.

10 Cut a long length of twine and wrap each end around an end of your stick, then tie to secure. Now hang your wind chimes outside or by a window. When the wind blows, the pictures will move and the chimes will make noises!

Tips, Tricks and Twists

🍃 If you can't find bamboo, you could use fallen sticks from your local park or woods.

🍃 What else could you add to your wind chimes? Experiment with tying on bottle tops, beads or empty pots. What different noises do they make in the wind?

Lots of Leaves

Try different ways of making jungle leaves with paints, crayons and paper!

Leaf Prints

You will need:

Real leaves
A4 card
Paints
A paintbrush

What to do:

1 Ask a grown-up to help you to collect some real leaves. Try to find different shapes and sizes.

2 Cover the bumpy side of a leaf in paint. You can choose any colour you like.

3 Press the painted side of the leaf down on a piece of card then gently peel it off to leave a perfect print!

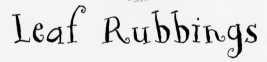

Leaf Rubbings

You will need:

Real leaves
Thin white A4 paper
Crayons

What to do:

1 Ask a grown-up to help you collect some real leaves.

2 Lay a leaf on a table with the bumpy side facing up, then place a piece of thin paper over the top.

3 Rub your crayon over the paper and watch a picture of your leaf appear!

Paper Leaves

You will need:

Green A4 paper
A pencil
Safety scissors

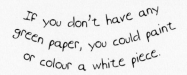

If you don't have any green paper, you could paint or colour a white piece.

What to do:

1 Fold a sheet of A4 paper in half so the short sides meet, then in half again, then one more time.

2 Open up the paper, then cut along the fold lines to make eight rectangles.

3 Fold all the rectangles in half, from one long edge to the other.

4 Draw half a leaf on each folded rectangle – or make up your own shapes. Make sure the shaped edge of your leaf goes on the unfolded side of the rectangle. You can copy or trace the leaves on the back of your sticker sheet.

5 Cut out each shaped edge, leaving the folded side. Unfold the rectangles to reveal your leaves!

Tips, Tricks and Twists

🍃 You could use all these leaves to make an amazing jungle collage, or as a background for the Pasta Pictures on pages 16 and 17. Try painting on some bright flowers, too!

🍃 How about making your own wrapping paper with a pattern of leaf prints?

Grow Your Own Jungle

Make your very own miniature jungle, filled with real plants!

You will need:

A large box or tub
Small stones, pebbles
  or gravel
A gardening trowel
Soil
Small plants (see next
  page)
Fallen moss (optional)
Small branches or
  bamboo canes
A sheet of card
Pens or pencils
Safety scissors
Varnish
A paintbrush
String
Lolly sticks
Sticky tape

Prepare your container:

Try an old washing-up bowl or a large plastic tub. It needs to be waterproof.

1 Line your container with 2–3cm
  of gravel or small stones. This is so that
  when you water your jungle
  the water can drain away
  and not stay in the soil.

Plants don't like it when soil stays too wet.

2 Use your trowel to add soil on top of the
  stones almost up to the top of the container,
  Leave 2–3cm at the top.

3 Pat down your soil with the
  back of the trowel so it's not
  too loose. Add a little more soil
  if you need to top it up, then pat
  down again.

4 Poke your branches or bamboo canes
  into the soil at the back of your container,
  so they stand upright.

How about taking a trip to the woods or a park, to see if you can find any fallen moss or branches to use?

Plants:

Ferns and succulents work well, because they look like small jungle trees and plants – but you can use any plants you like. Here's what we used:

Peace lily
Maidenhair fern
String of hearts
Calathea
Miniature succulents

Add your plants:

1 Choose which plants to add to your jungle! Look at the box on the left for suggestions.

2 Stick your finger in the soil and wiggle it around to make a long, thin hole.

3 Carefully take your first plant and gently place its roots into the hole. Push in the soil around it so the plant is held in place. All the roots should be in the soil and the green part of the plant should be above the soil. Ask a grown-up to help you!

4 Repeat steps 2 and 3 with your other plants, until they are all planted in the soil.

Leave a little space in between your plants, so they have some room to grow!

5 Fill in any empty spaces in the soil with a few spare pebbles, sticks or some fallen moss.

6 Twist a trailing or climbing plant such as ivy around your branches or bamboo canes so it looks like jungle vines. Or you could twist green pipe cleaners around, instead.

Add your animals:

1 Draw some jungle animals on a piece of card, then colour them in. You could use your stickers if you prefer, or copy the templates on the back of your sticker sheet. Cut them out.

2 Paint a coat of varnish, such as PVA glue, over your animals and leave to dry. This will help keep them waterproof.

3 Ask a grown-up to poke a small hole in the top of the animals you want to hang up.

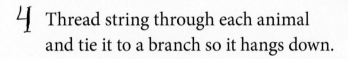

4 Thread string through each animal and tie it to a branch so it hangs down.

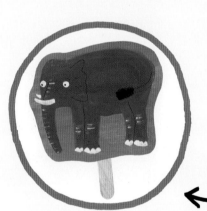

5 Ask your grown-up to cut your lolly sticks in half, then tape a piece to the back of each of the animals you want to stand up. Stick each one gently into your soil.

Tips, Tricks and Twists

🍃 Don't forget to water your jungle. Every few days, feel the soil to see how dry it is. If it has dried out, give your plants a small drink of water. Your succulents will need less water than the other plants.

🍃 Take the animals out of your jungle before you water it!

🍃 Place your jungle in a sunny spot. Plants need lots of sunlight to keep them healthy and happy.

First published 2020 by Macmillan Children's Books
an imprint of Pan Macmillan
The Smithson, 6 Briset Street, London EC1M 5NR
Associated companies throughout the world
www.panmacmillan.com

ISBN: 978-1-5290-2384-8

1 3 5 7 9 8 6 4 2

A CIP catalogue record for this book is available from the British Library.

Printed in China.

Monkey Pop-up Card

Jungle Wind Chimes

Here are some extra stickers to decorate your crafts.

You might find these templates helpful when making some of your crafts.
Have a look on page 3 to find out how to use them.

Butterfly Paper Chains

Lots of Leaves

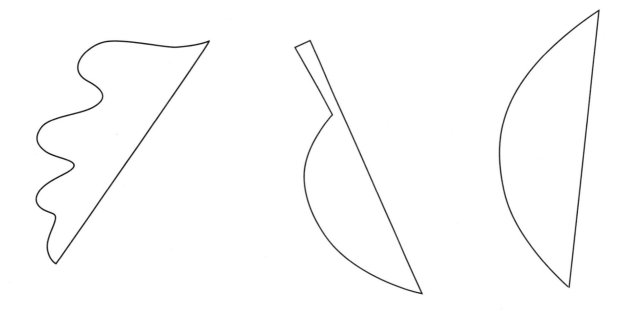

You can copy these outlines to make animal pictures to use in the
Guess the Animal Game and Grow Your Own Jungle.

Grow Your Own Jungle

You can use these stickers to make patterns to decorate your crafts.

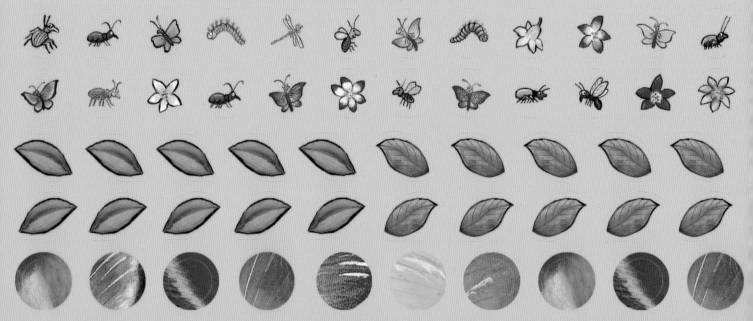

These eyes will come in handy for lots of your crafts, like the Butterfly Wings, Wiggling Caterpillar and more.

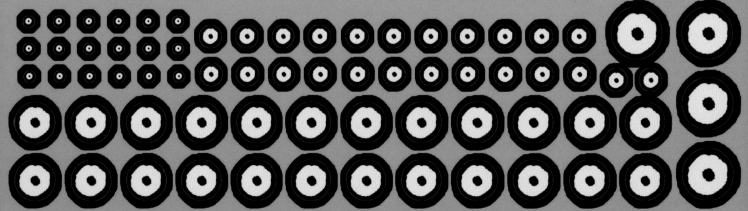